Wondermo.

LOM
ART

Illustrated by

Kerby Rosanes

This book belongs to

....

Edited by Hannah Daffern
and Lauren Farnsworth
Designed by Derrian Bradder
Cover Design by Zoe Bradley

With thanks to Harry Thornton
for being a great talent scout

First published in Great Britain in 2020 by LOM ART, an imprint of
Michael O'Mara Books Limited, 9 Lion Yard, Tremadoc Road, London SW4 7NQ

The material in this book previously appeared in *Fantomorphia: An Extreme Colouring and Search Challenge* and
Geomorphia: An Extreme Colouring and Search Challenge.

W www.mombooks.com/lom   f Michael O'Mara Books   𝕏 @OMaraBooks   📷 @lomartbooks

Copyright © Michael O'Mara Books Limited 2018, 2020

A CIP catalogue record for this book is available from the British Library.

ISBN: 978-1-912785-37-7

1 3 5 7 9 10 8 6 4 2

This book was printed in China.

FSC
www.fsc.org
MIX
Paper from
responsible sources
FSC® C010256

Explore this fantastical colouring adventure!

Dive into my super-detailed, enchanting fantasy world, where dream becomes reality, and objects and animals inspired by gothic grandeur and natural landscapes morph into captivatingly complex scenes.

Each drawing has been crafted with fineliner pens and can be coloured in any way you like.

Keep your wits about you to find search objects scattered throughout the pages. You'll find a list of these hidden gems at the back of the book, so you know exactly what to look for, along with all the answers.

Kerby Rosanes

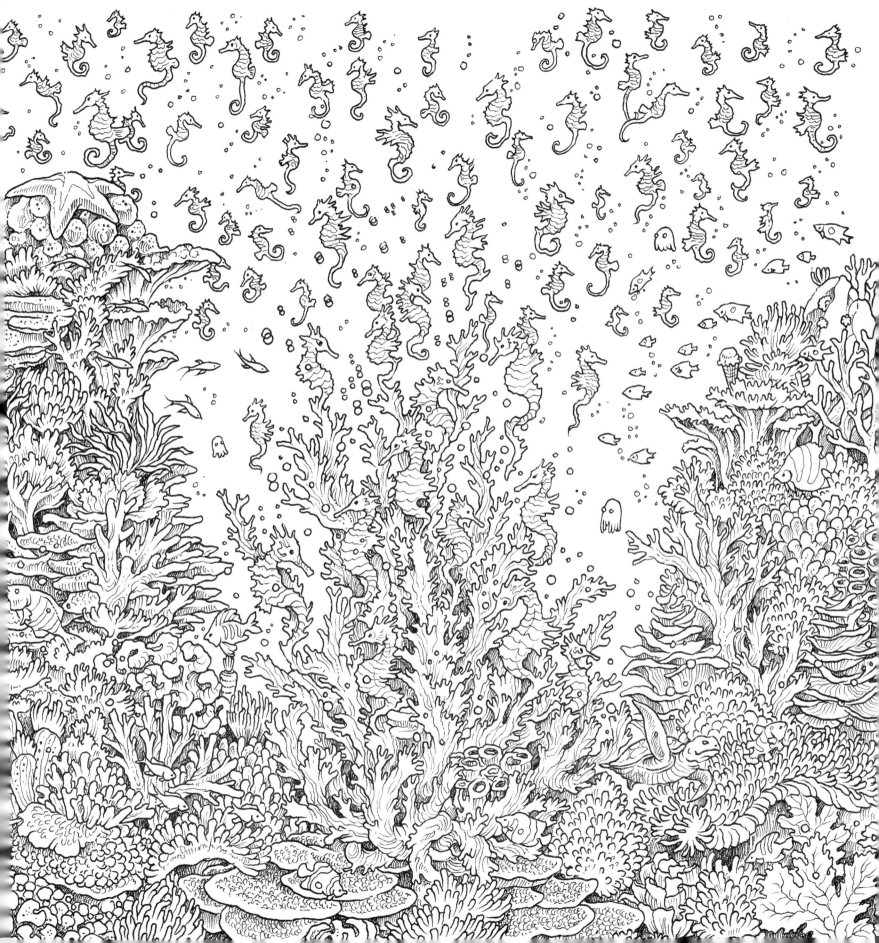

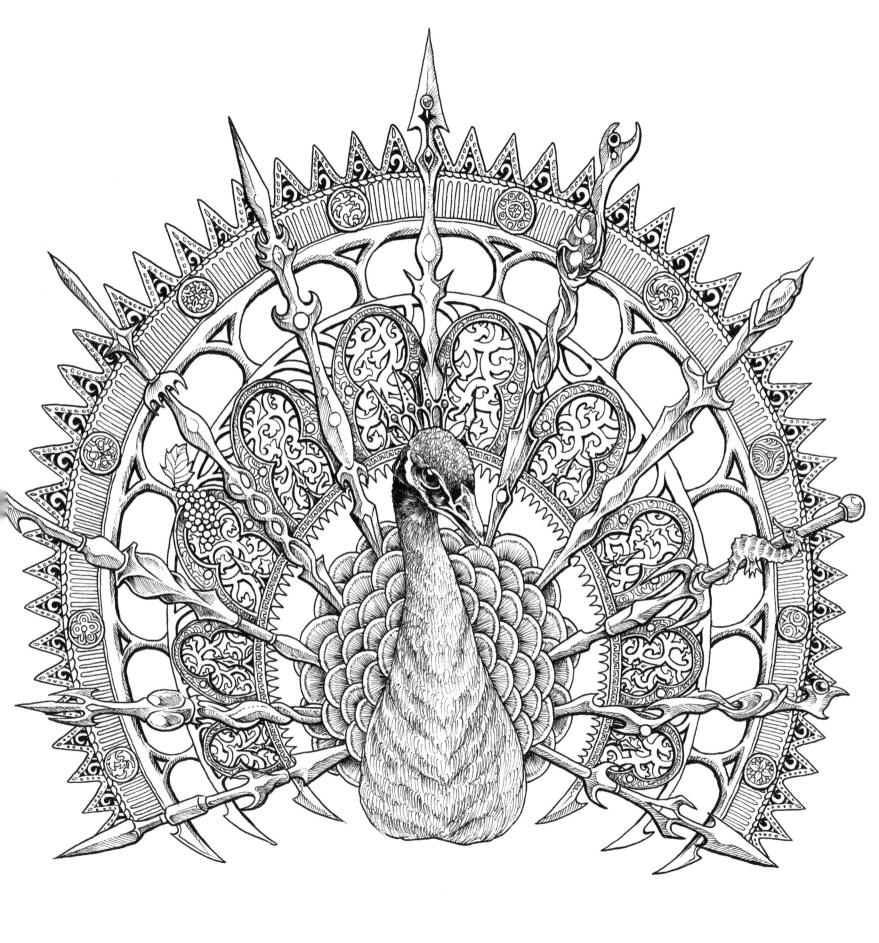

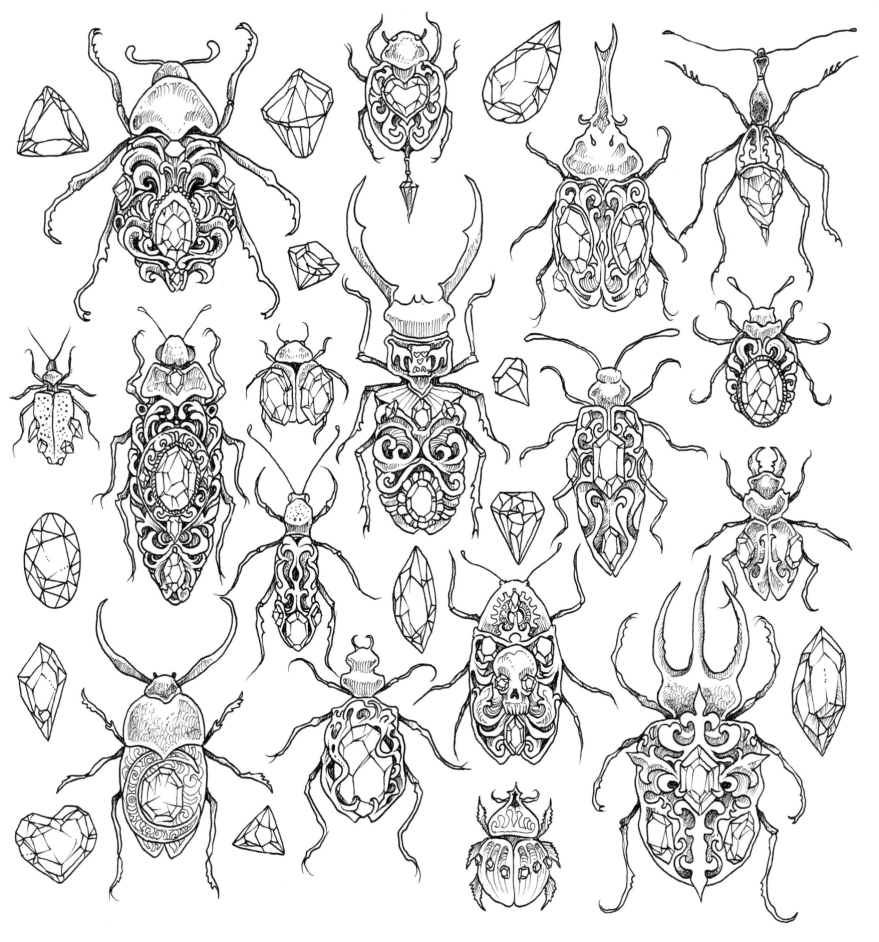

Can you find these items, artefacts and creatures in the book?

This camera

The Four of Diamonds

This watering can

This umbrella

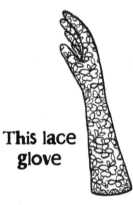

This lace glove

This mouse

This hot-air balloon

The Five of Diamonds

This crescent moon

This light bulb

This pocket watch

The Four of Hearts

This clockwork spider

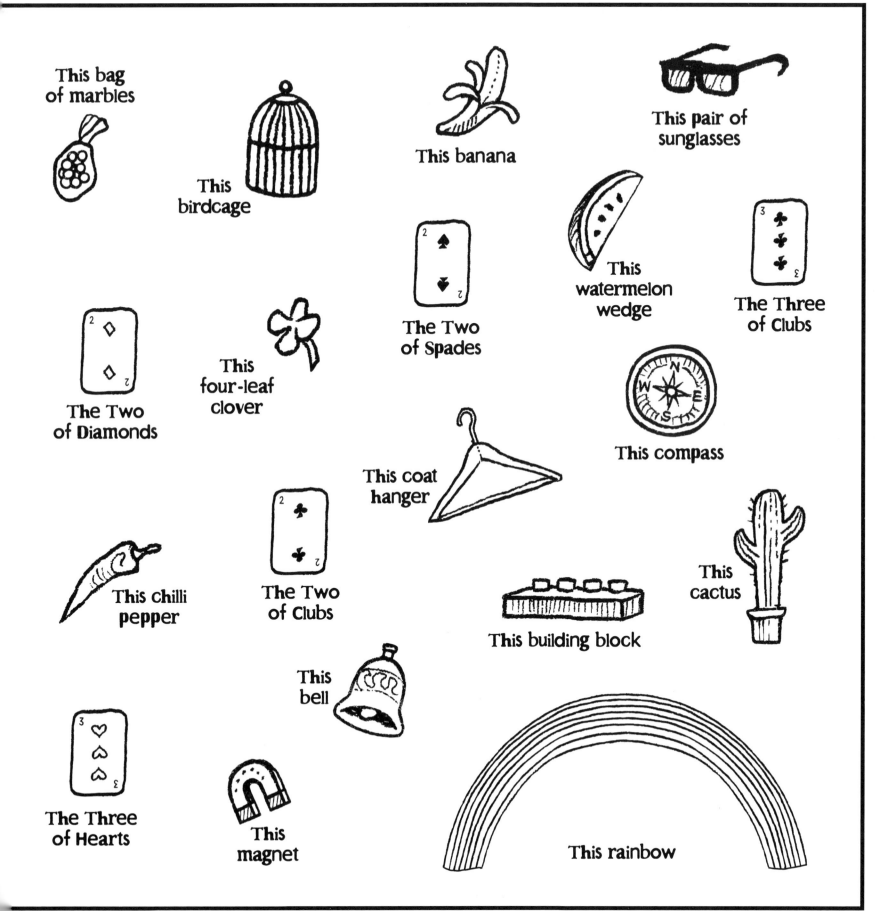

This *Stegosaurus*

This bouquet
of flowers

The Three
of Spades

This tennis ball

The Three of
Diamonds

This **pair of**
odd socks

This ice
cream

This
toothbrush

The Two
of Hearts

These steampunk
goggles

This **padlock**

This
megaphone

This corn on
the cob

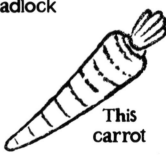

This
carrot

This top hat

The Five
of Clubs

This teacup
and saucer

This unicorn

The Four
of Spades

This
box

This
lantern

The Five
of Spades

This
starfish

This rabbit

This
jewel-eyed
skull

This miniature
portrait

This black
cat

This
pentagram

This fairy

The Four
of Clubs

The Five
of Hearts

This cupcake

This
rattlesnake

This puffin

This bunch
of grapes

This trumpet

This
teddy
bear

This
gnome

This full moon

This
hamster

This seahorse

This
acorn

This pyramid

This
strawberry

Steampunk goggles
and the Four of Hearts

A birdcage and a toothbrush

Rattlesnake and the Five of Clubs

A chilli pepper and a four-leaf clover

An acorn and the Four of Diamonds

A bell and the Three of Hearts

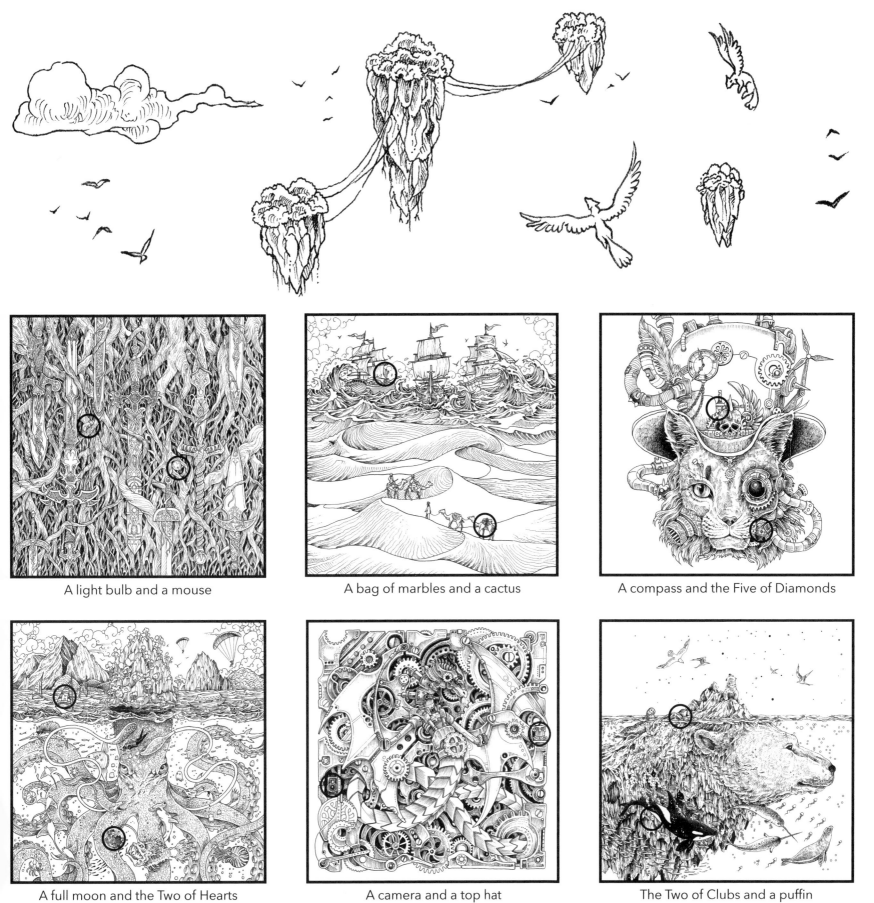

A light bulb and a mouse

A bag of marbles and a cactus

A compass and the Five of Diamonds

A full moon and the Two of Hearts

A camera and a top hat

The Two of Clubs and a puffin

A pyramid and a hot-air balloon

A banana and the Three of Clubs

A miniature portrait
and a teacup and saucer

A rainbow and the Three of Diamonds

A lantern and the Five of Spades

A corn on the cob and a *Stegosaurus*

A pocket watch and a pentagram

A padlock and the Two of Diamonds

A lace glove and an umbrella

A carrot and an ice cream

A crescent moon
and the Four of Spades

A megaphone and the Two of Spades

A unicorn and a black cat

A pair of sunglasses and
a wedge of watermelon

A gnome and a rabbit

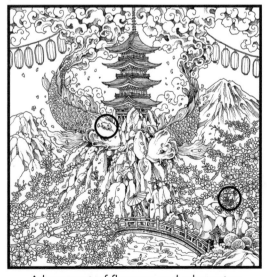

A bouquet of flowers and a hamster

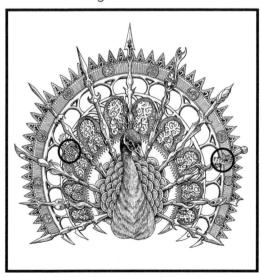

A bunch of grapes and a seahorse

A building block and a magnet

A starfish and the Four of Clubs

A coat hanger and a teddy bear

A clockwork spider
and a strawberry

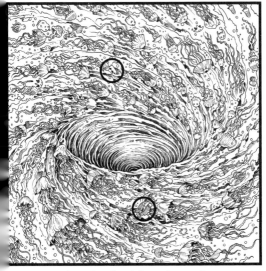

A pair of odd socks and
the Three of Spades

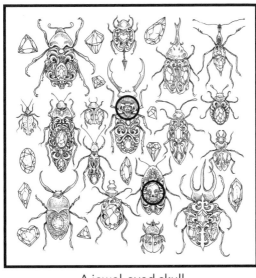

A jewel-eyed skull
and the Five of Hearts

A cupcake and a trumpet

A box and a fairy

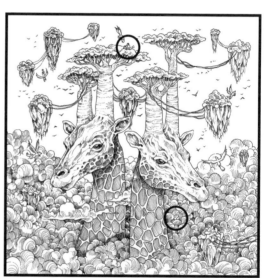

A tennis ball and a watering can

The end

www.kerbyrosanes.com

@kerbyrosanes

@kerbyrosanes